ISBN-13: 978-0-545-15917-3

ISBN-10: 0-545-15917-2

12 11 10 9 8 7 6 5 4 3 2 1   9 10 11 12 13 14/0

Printed in the U.S.A.   08

This edition first printing, January 2009

The illustrations were created by pouring colored
cotton fiber through hand-cut stencils.

Book design by Denise Fleming and David Powers

For David, still the one

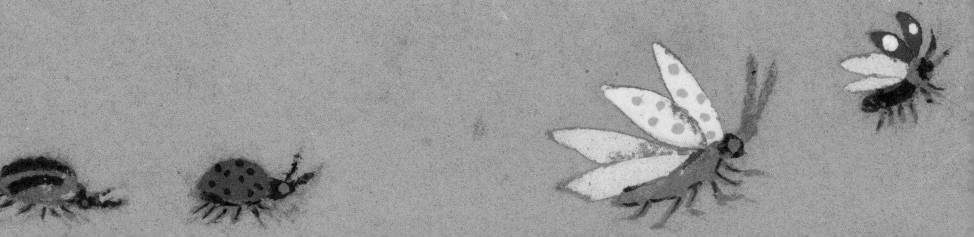

SCHOLASTIC INC.
New York Toronto London Auckland Sydney
Mexico City New Delhi Hong Kong Buenos Aires

DENISE FLEMING

beetle
bop

Striped
beetles,

spotted
beetles,

all-over-dotted
beetles.

Brown beetles, green beetles, not-often-seen beetles.

BuZZing beetles,

humming beetles,

steadily drumming beetles.

Big beetles,

small **beetles**,

crawl-up-the-wall **beetles.**

chewing beetles,
sawing beetles,

noisily

gnawing

beetles.

Round beetles,
square beetles,
fly-in-the-air beetles.
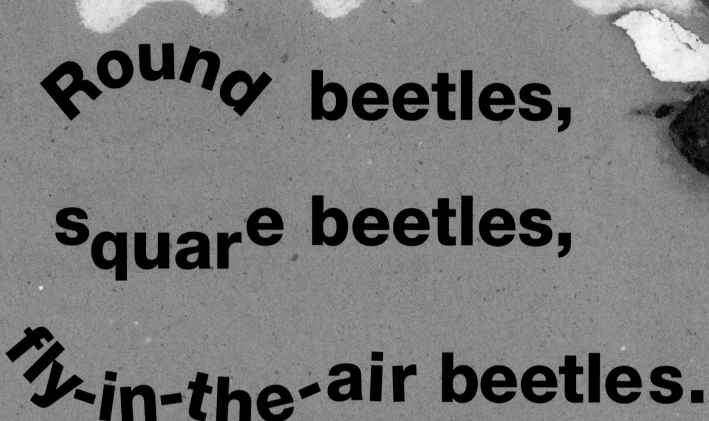

Bark beetles, sand beetles,

fill-up-your-hand

beetles.

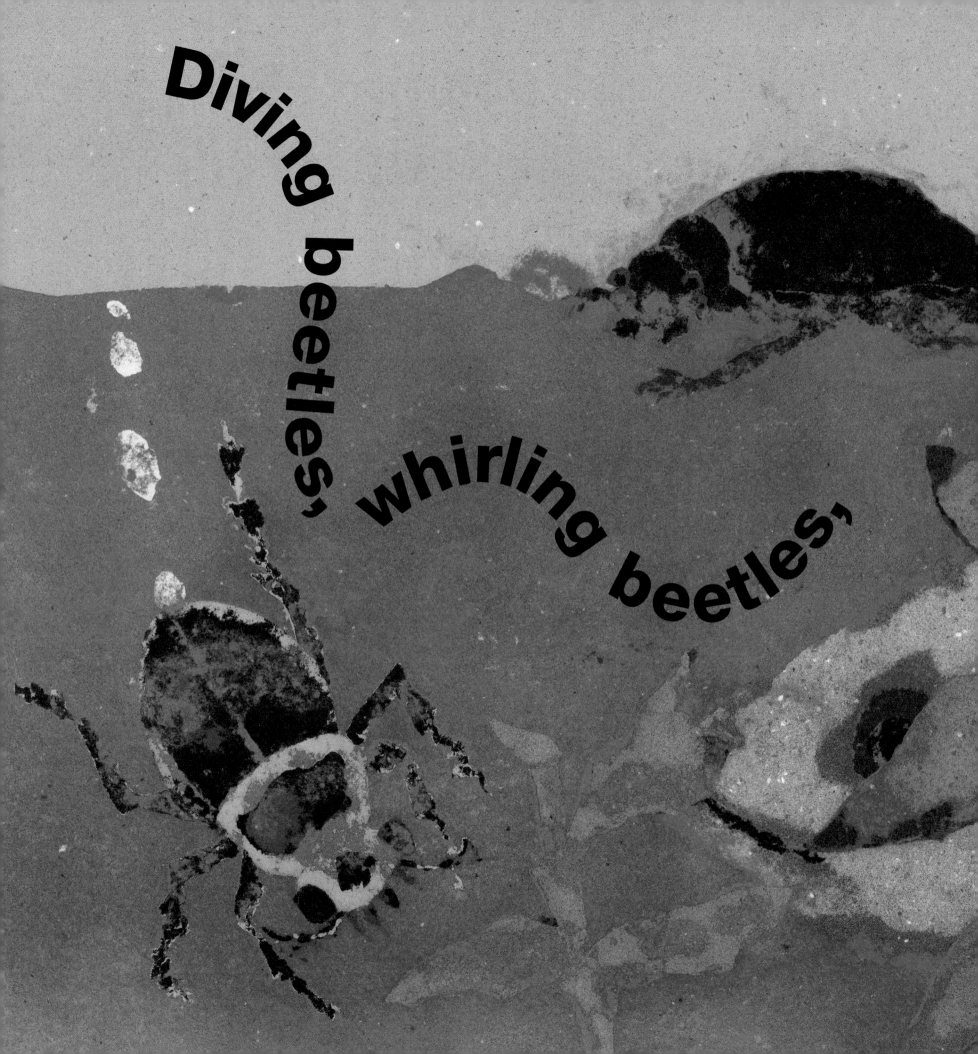

Diving beetles, whirling beetles,

spiraling, swirling beetles.

Blue beetles, black beetles,

hide-in-the-crack beetles.

Glowing beetles,
flashing beetles,

constantly crashing
beetles.

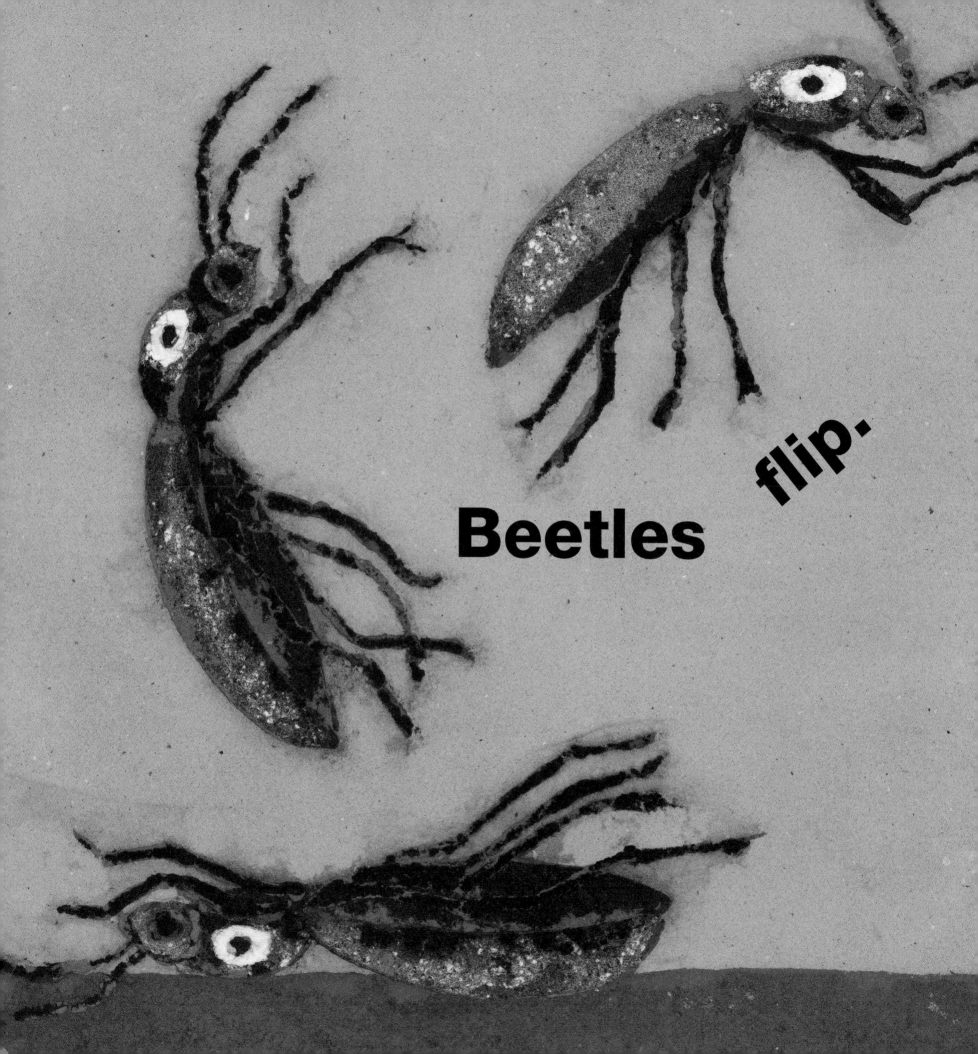

Beetles flip.

Beetles flop.

Beetles fly.

Beetles...

Beetles live in forests, deserts, mountains, and ponds. They come in many different shapes, sizes, colors, and patterns. But all beetles have three body segments and six legs, and almost all have two sets of wings—a front set that protects the second set, which is used for flying.

Beetles are one of the largest groups of animals on earth. Some are pests, some are friends.

What kinds of **beetles** live near you?